Author Danyel Baker
Cover design by Hive 180

MW00633740

DISCLAIMER

The information provided in this workbook is designed to provide helpful information and motivation to our readers. It is sold with the understanding that the author and publisher are not engaged to render any psychological, legal, or any other kind of professional advice. No warranties or guarantees are expressed or implied by the author's or publisher's choice to include any of the content. Neither the publisher nor the author shall be liable for any physical, psychological, emotional, financial, or commercial damages, including, but not limited to, special, incidental, consequential or other damages. Our views and rights are the same: You are responsible for your own choices, actions, and results.

Published by Danyel Baker
© 2018 United States
ISBN 978-0-692-16379-5

DEDICATION

To ALL of my family
May HAPPYness flow from
ABOVE—DOWN—INSIDE—OUT

I love you deeply

Thank you Lord for this beautiful life You have blessed me with.
An amazing husband to show me there is always more to give, and
always more that can be done to be better. Who's constant search for
growth within himself has inspired me to grow and share with the
world that HAPPYness is for everyone. Thank you Lord for ALL my
children who are my constant reminder of why I am on this earth.
Each of you have a huge piece of my heart.

We ALL can make a difference in the world if we choose to.

-Danyel Baker

Preface

Have you ever asked yourself, "Why am I not happy?" Or, maybe told yourself, "I'll be happy when . . ." If these words have gone through your mind, then the information you will find here can probably help you! There is nothing wrong with you, you CAN be happy, you've just been looking in the wrong direction. You've been looking for the "things" in your outside world to "make" you happy. Or maybe you've been asking yourself the wrong questions like, "Why am I not happy?", which focuses your attention on the negative of "what's wrong". You need to look within yourself, and this workbook will show you how!

Knowing we all have had some form of struggle in our lives, varying in extremes, means we can all relate in one way or another. We all have felt some sort of pain that each of us handle in different ways. You may wonder what happens in other people's lives that they seek out ways to "get over", "get through", "move on" or "overcome" their past. The truth is, everyone has a different reason, and it shouldn't matter WHY they are searching, but rather that they CHOOSE to BEGIN searching for a more positive way to live. Stay clear from comparing ourselves to others and the "who had it worse" or "of course they're happy because they have that" mentality. Our goal here is to be the best form of ourselves that we can be. The key is to know that it doesn't matter how extreme your struggle was, the choice is YOURS on how you decide to move on and live the rest of your life. This is why I'm choosing to focus on the positive changes we can ALL achieve with this workbook. You no longer have to be a victim of your past, but instead, you can be a superhero to your future!

Let's work through this together over the next 30 days! Apply what you learn every day by taking ACTION with the steps you will read in this workbook, then FEEL the change that will transform your world.

It's time to develop your new strength...HAPPYness!

Throughout my life, people have asked me, "How can you be so happy all the time?" In times where most people would become sad or depressed or get down on themselves about what has happened to them, I was always able to remain positive and happy by focusing on the good that I saw in that circumstance or what good was going to come out of it. Well, for years I couldn't tell them "how", I just "was". I couldn't explain it, I just did it!

Over the last 15 years of my life, I've attended motivational and inspirational seminars with people helping others achieve their dreams. I've read books about different ways to attract what you want into your life and pushing yourself to be the best version of you.

These seminars and books used positive affirmations and kept you focused on what you want in your future instead of what went wrong in your past. Using these philosophies, I put together a workbook that is easy to understand and easy to use in a fun way to create great new habits to create a great new YOU!

From a young age, I've used these methods without realizing this was actually a "strategy" that has been around much longer than I have. I just always felt in my heart that I'd rather be smiling and HAPPY no matter what happened in my life.

This doesn't mean I've never cried or had negative thoughts! I have, but the difference was, I didn't let what happened to me dictate how the rest of my day or week or month or year or LIFE was going to go . . . and you don't have to either!

This book idea came to me while I was at one of the motivational seminars I often attend. I wanted a way to give back to the world and share with others what I knew. Gosh, if this worked for me, it could work for others too!

I want to spread HAPPYness, and this workbook is how I am going to do it! All you have to do is stick with this concept for 30 Days!

Author's Note

Yes, I know HAPPYness is spelled wrong. However, I didn't want to take the word "HAPPY" out, so, this is what you will see throughout this workbook. It is incredibly important to visually see this word while you take this journey.

I also realize that this word is repeated A LOT, and there is a great reason for that too. It's quite simple, actually: the more you say and think about something, the more likely it will happen to you. It's called the Law of Attraction. People have written about this phenomenon for years and I can give you a great example that I know has happened to everyone.

Have you ever been thinking of a friend and then that friend calls or you see them somewhere? And then you say what?! "Oh, my gosh, I was just thinking about you!" Well, there you have it, that is the basic Law of Attraction. What you think about, you bring about. Which also means, the more you see the word HAPPYness, the more you say the word HAPPYness, the more you think about the word HAPPYness, the more likely you will feel it in your life.

I know what you're thinking, "How can just saying some simple words change my life?", and I can totally understand that question. But, how about if you say those words in a more positive way with a knowing attitude. More like, "Saying these words can change my life!" Remember your mind and thoughts are powerful, and it will be demonstrated on this journey. You HAVE to believe! I understand you may feel like this is ridiculous and it will never work for you . . . BUT WHAT IF IT DOES? I believe you can and YOU have to believe you will. It's a minimal investment and a 30-day commitment that can be transforming in every aspect of your life. This workbook will tell you how to achieve what you want. As you release negativity from your life and stop holding on to your past, you will begin to feel and see changes occurring within you and around you. Repeat this statement out loud, I am letting go of all negativity and I am ready for HAPPYness in my life. The more you say these words, the more you'll believe them, so repeat as often as you can.

INTRODUCTION

In this workbook, you will use a 30 day challenge, or discipline, concept. With this format, we are creating new habits for ourselves with small simple steps that lead to significant changes in our lives. Although we cannot control completely what happens to us through the day, we can control how we handle the situation and how it affects the rest of our day by CHOOSING to be HAPPY. This will be a challenge where you will need to be very disciplined.

Its purpose is to reprogram your mind and body to create great habits and a better YOU! The wonderful thing about these 30-day disciplines is you can do it with anything, for example, 30 days of exercise, 30 days of great nutrition, or here's a good one, 30 days of no TV!!! AHH . . . say what? Don't get all freaked out. I'm not making you do this, these are just examples of some of the things we have done. But imagine what you could accomplish during that TV time, hmmm. Anyway, by doing a 30-day discipline, you WILL create better habits in your life that will send you into a positive forward motion.

For the next 30 days, YOU CHOOSE HAPPYness! Even though you may (or may not) consider yourself a happy person to begin with, everyone can use more HAPPYness in their lives, and just as important, to share it with others! The main purpose of this workbook is to keep it simple so that ANYONE can understand it, from kids to adults, and then put the contents you learn to great use. Also, this is called a workbook for a reason. You will have to "work" your mind along with daily SIMPLE "action steps" to help ingrain what you're learning. When your mind (thoughts) and body (actions) work as a team, the results are much faster than just working one or the other.

Enjoy your journey!

HAPPYness IS JUST A THOUGHT UNTIL YOU PUT IT INTO ACTION.

All right.....I'm gonna get all Dr. Seuss on you now! I wrote this poem because it really shares everything we are going to accomplish in this workbook, AND it was FUN....which is how this process is intended for you!

Cut out the poem (tear out the page) and tape it on your bathroom mirror.
Read this every morning and night while you brush your teeth :)

As I look in the mirror
who do I see?
A person with desire
to become incredibly HAPPY.
I open my heart,
I open my mind,
I attract all that's positive,
I leave the negative behind.
Forget about the past
the present is where I'll be,
I'll find new ways
to share my great energy.
My thoughts move me forward
I'm dedicated to success,
motivated by my vision
to be at my best.
Improving myself
little steps at a time,
progressing daily
creating my new mind.
Being "All In"
is what it will take,
attacking my goals
so make no mistake.
I choose to be HAPPY
it comes from within,
I am in charge
of how, where and when.
I will share with others
and show them how,
HAPPYness can change
their lives starting NOW.

How To Use This Workbook

Read a HAPPYness challenge page from this workbook every morning before starting your day, and then take the "Action Step" to fulfill your challenge.

Read the inspirational quotes (as often as possible) that are throughout this workbook, and let them inspire your mind and your heart. The more you say and think HAPPYness, the more it will fill your life. It would be ideal for you to have this workbook with you at all times so you can read your affirmations throughout the day and write down all the positive thoughts you get. If this isn't possible, then write down what you need or take a snap shot on your phone, whatever is most convenient for you. It's important to have this handy to keep you motivated and your mind in the right place.

Then, use the extra space on the pages to write down creative thoughts, ideas or drawings that come to you. I bet the more you write or draw, the more will come your way because you're in an accepting and creative state of mind.

If you have a HAPPY thought,
WRITE IT DOWN . . . ANYTIME . . . ANYWHERE.
This is HAPPYness talking to YOU!

Day 1

YOUR JOURNEY STARTS HERE!

Read this quote and really think about what HAPPYness means to you —THEN OBTAIN IT!!!

"Attract what you expect,
Reflect what you desire,
Become what you respect,
Mirror what you admire."
—Anonymous

Welcome HAPPYness

I open myself up to HAPPYness and WELCOME it into my life. I deserve all that it will bring me.

ACTION STEP

Grab a small note pad (preferably sticky pad) and write "I Welcome HAPPYness" on each sheet. Stick or tape them everywhere you will see them throughout the day. Put them on doors, windows, mirrors, in your car, in your locker at school or work, on your desk. These little notes will help you to remember your action for today, which is reminding yourself that you "Welcome HAPPYness" into your life. Have FUN!

The secret to getting ahead is getting started.
—Mark Twain

To experience GROWTH, we must exhibit positive, forward-moving CHANGE.

Day 2

THINK HAPPYness

What I THINK about, I bring about. It's that simple! Your thoughts are extremely powerful and the more you feed and control positive thoughts into your mind, the more it becomes your reality.

What you think, you become.
—Buddha

ACTION STEP

Think deeply about all that makes you happy. For me, I love watching the sun rise and set with my loved ones. I love taking walks and going on adventures with my husband and kids, or hopping in the car and just seeing where we end up. These little things make me happy and I am so incredibly thankful for these precious moments I get to spend with them.

What is it for you? Don't think too hard about it, find a space on this page and write down the first couple things that come to your mind. Then, write a sentence of gratitude using what you love to do and makes you HAPPY. Writing the thoughts down on paper, acknowledging them, and reading them aloud will help bring you more of these moments. It solidifies what you want, what you enjoy and what makes you HAPPY. Read what you wrote throughout the day.

Here's mine . . . I am so incredibly grateful for all the adventures I get to have with my family. It gives us such valuable and quality time together, making wonderful memories we can carry with us for the rest of our lives. It's these moments that make me HAPPY.

**Something beautiful is on the horizon....
MY HAPPYness**

Day 3

BELIEVE HAPPYness

I BELIEVE in my HAPPYness every day. It's right here for me! Every moment I spend believing will propel me in the right direction of my ultimate goal.

ACTION STEP

Write down one positive trait that you like about yourself. Staying positive about yourself is very important to your HAPPYness. So many people focus on the things they don't like about themselves and this negativity will create a downward spiral that only YOU CAN STOP! Don't get me wrong, self-criticism can be motivating if you choose your words wisely and take action to change the personality attributes that need some work.

If you can get a bit lazy, stay away from saying/writing the word lazy, which is negative. The self-motivating sentence will go like this, "I am motivated to stay productive throughout my day." By keeping the wording positive, you will enhance your self-motivation to get more stuff done in your day. Stay with personality attributes because these are the ones that can hold us back OR MOVE US FORWARD. Your mind can even help you with some physical attributes you want to improve on, like nutritious food and exercise to keep your body healthy. Don't sit there and ponder all the things you don't like about yourself. We ALL have something, but remain focused on the great things about yourself, because I know we ALL have these too. ;) By acknowledging the wonderful things about you, it's basically telling yourself you want more wonderful things to focus on . . . and guess what? They will come, your list of positives will start growing. You will see more and more great things about yourself that you never thought you had, and others will see it in you too! Take action on yourself to become a better YOU! Read your words throughout the day.

I believe in the person I want to become.
—Lana Del Rey

I AM HAPPYness.

Day 4

CHOOSE HAPPYness

HAPPYness IS a choice, so I make it MY choice! I CHOOSE for this amazing gift to be in my life!

ACTION STEP

This might be the most difficult action step for some people, controlling your emotions, but I know you're up for the challenge! How do I know this? Because you CHOSE to start this journey in the first place, which means, you want and are ready for change in your life! You want HAPPYness. Now, you must CHOOSE HAPPYness!

Throughout your day, you're given so many choices: what you're going to eat, what you're going to wear, what you're going to do today. These choices are relatively simple. Now, what is your natural choice when something goes wrong? Example, a stranger, a friend or a family member does/says something that makes you mad, sad or frustrated. Do you tend to hang onto that emotion for the rest of your day and let that feeling dictate how the rest of your day goes? Letting your emotions take control of your life would be the EASY choice for sure. Your emotions are powerful, yes, but your mind is more powerful and can overcome these negative feelings.
Here is a story my husband shared with me years ago. I don't know where it originated but it gives a great narrative of how powerful our minds are.

The Wise Old Indian

One evening, an old Cherokee Indian Chief told his grandson a story about a battle that goes on inside of everyone's mind.

He said, "My son, the battle is between two "wolves" inside us all. One is Evil. It is anger, envy, jealousy, sorrow, regret, greed, arrogance, self-pity, guilt, resentment, inferiority, lies, false pride, superiority, and ego. The other is Good. It is Happiness, peace, love, hope, truth, serenity, humility, kindness, empathy, generosity, compassion, and faith."

The grandson thought about it for a minute and then asked his grandfather, "Which wolf wins?"

The old Cherokee simply replied, "The one you feed."

Wow, I love that! It's your choice! YOU get to choose which emotions to feed. I'm not saying you can't EVER be angry or sad, all these emotions are what makes us human and that is incredible. But let your emotions drive you to better yourself, not bring you down. If you're hit with an emotion that can cloud over your day, it will be hard to control yourself at first, but it's YOUR CHOICE to decide how you're going to carry on! Things go wrong or not according to plan all the time. But, that surely doesn't mean you have to let it get you down and possibly affect the decisions you make for the rest of the day/week/month. When you will "get over it" is entirely up to you. How long are you going to drag out your misery?

Like I said, this can be the most difficult challenge for some, but typically, whatever is the most difficult for you, is often the most important in your life for growth.

Change my thoughts and I'll change my world!
—Norman Vincent Peale

Day 5

EXPECT HAPPYness

EXPECT HAPPYness everyday! By EXPECTING something this great to happen to you......your strong, positive will and expectation for this will become a reality. Say to yourself out loud, (quietly if needed), "I expect HAPPYness in my life today.", and say this as often as possible. Gosh, saying these words makes me feel like a kid waking up on Christmas morning, when you know somethings coming although you don't know when or what.....but it's coming! The excitement and anticipation of "The Surprise"! This is what saying these words should feel like to you! Remember to look and feel for every little simple "surprise" that makes you smile, because HAPPYness comes in all forms, even the sunshine on your face :)

It's my time to be HAPPY

ACTION STEP

Expecting great things to happen to us everyday, like HAPPYness (or anything) is a tremendous quality to have. It's a training tool for your mind to overcome mediocrity, which is settling or being satisfied for what life "gives" us. You still want to be grateful for everything you have, and you should, but this thought process will open the door to greater things in every aspect of your life, as simple or as big as they come. Be sure to use the "UNexpected gifts" as lessons to prepare you and to achieve your EXPECTED HAPPYness. Repeat to yourself as often as possible, "I expect HAPPYness in my life today!" Now go "expect" great things for your day!

Day 6

DECIDE HAPPYness

I DECIDE to have HAPPYness become part of my life. This is MY time! This SHOULD be an easy decision for you to make, but in order for you to make this happen, you MUST stop lingering in INDECISION about important things in your life! Some things are easy to figure out what the right choice is, and some, can be more difficult because we want to do the right thing SO badly. HOWEVER, if we don't make any decision at all, where does that leave you? In the same spot.... NOWHERE! Which means no growth for you! Even if you don't make the "right" decision, you can recalculate and keep going. At least you are still actively participating in your life by making some decision. Nobody is ever right ALL the time, but the successful people learn from it and keep pushing, because now you know, and you can learn from that life experience. So....are you going to linger or move forward? The diagram below is just a visual I came up with so you can see the forward progression of making ANY decision versus no decision at all.

DECIDE....My HAPPYness depends on it!

Decision Making Diagram
(The flow of this chart is from bottom to top indicating upward growth)

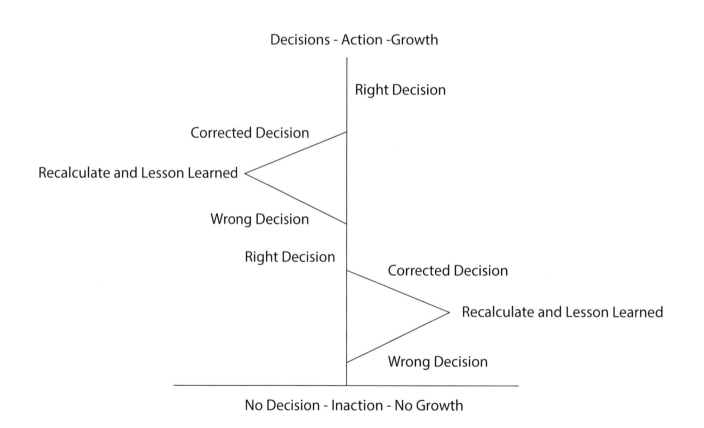

ACTION STEP 1
(Yes there are two today)

Look up the word Decide, I used dictionary.com, and read the definition. OK, I wrote it for you down below, ONLY because its important for you to take action now for this process. Read it a few times....I want you to feel these words in your heart. When you decide that HAPPYness is the choice you want in your life, this is your first victory.

I also added some synonyms and antonyms. Read the definition first, then the synonyms and then the antonyms.

What's the biggest difference you see between the synonyms and the antonyms? I see that some are positive action words and some are negative NON action words. Read them all and then DECIDE how you want to be in your life! Circle what you want!

Decision—The act, process or need for making up one's mind.
To solve or conclude; To determine or settle.

Synonyms	Antonyms
Agree	Delay
Choose	Hesitate
Determine	Postpone
Elect	Procrastinate
Establish	Put off
Select	Defer

ACTION STEP 2

Now that you have the hang of how this "decision making process" works, lets do one more.

What is ONE thing you need to make a decision about? Take 60 seconds and ask yourself this...

Which decision will add the most value to my life (and others) to move me furthest in the direction I want to go?

This question is to help you take action and move forward. If you need to recalculate, do so, just keep moving and keep making those decisions!

Look over the "Decision Making" diagram again and know that ONLY by making a decision will you continue progress.

Day 7

VISUALIZE HAPPYness

Being able to VISUALIZE what you want is extremely beneficial to your personal growth development and motivation. Closing your eyes and picturing what you want to accomplish (in detail) "tricks" your mind into your dreams/goals becoming your reality. You will be surprised at how much faster you will get to your goals with daily visualization.

ACTION STEP

Spend a few minutes EVERY DAY when you wake visualizing positive things that WILL happen in your life that will give you more HAPPYness. Visualize each of your daily tasks getting done efficiently and having fun while doing it. Making this a part of your DAILY routine is so important! Waking up in the morning with positive thoughts will start your day out with the right intent. You can do this before getting out of bed, as long as you sit up so you aren't dozing in and out of sleep. You can even do it in the shower. Just do it, and do it with INTENT!

You will be surprised at how motivating yourself with positive thoughts each morning will actually energize you to attack your day with enthusiasm, because you have all those great thoughts to look forward to!

"There are only two options:
Make progress or make excuses."
—Tony Robbins

Day 8

UNDERSTAND HAPPYness

To UNDERSTAND HAPPYness is knowing that it is an energy out there for ANYONE and EVERYONE! Energy can also be transferred . . . So just as your HAPPYness can be shared with others, their HAPPYness can be shared with you.

Whoever is Happy will make others Happy too.
—Anne Frank

ACTION STEP

Share your HAPPYness with someone, even better, with more than one someone! Think of a person you know and send them a "Happy Note." It can be a card, a call, slip a little note under a door or into a locker, or a text. I like to click on Pinterest and search some fun little sayings and send them to people. It's so easy. Remember, we want to keep this journey simple and fun!

ACTION STEP 2

YES, there are two, again! Now, at some point today, you're going to share your HAPPYness with a stranger. WHAT?! YES, and again, this will be simple.

Here are some examples: Hold the door open for someone, give a compliment, smile and say, "Good morning" as they walk by, pay for someone's bridge toll if you commute. The list goes on and on. Who knows, you might just change their day, and that could change their LIFE!

Side note: HAPPYness should be shared from your heart without expecting anything in return. That is what makes this action step so special!

Side note 2: Yes, there are two of these, as well! When you're sharing with a stranger, be sure it can't be taken the wrong way, i.e., no creepiness! DO NOT STALK someone just to give them a compliment! There are MANY people out there that could use some of your HAPPYness! AGAIN, keep this simple, short and from your heart.

*Attitude is the Difference between an ordeal
and an adventure full of HAPPYness.*
—Bob Bitchin

Day 9

FEEL HAPPYness

I am in charge of how I feel...so I FEEL HAPPYness. This is truly an inside job....It starts in your heart! Remember, it's a feeling in your heart and can be controlled with your mind. I believe that God has given us ALL HAPPYness from birth with the first smile reflexes we get as infants. If we weren't supposed to be happy, then we wouldn't have the ability to smile!!! It's been within us the whole time, we just need to bring it out again. We are ALL given the ability to smile and to FEEL HAPPYness from the beginning of our lives, but as we get older, we start letting outside occurrences dictate how we feel and therefore STEAL our HAPPYness! So turn the corners of your mouth upward and start FEELING your HAPPYness the way God intended....IN YOUR HEART!

HAPPYness is Homemade by ME!

ACTION STEP

Think how you would describe the feeling of HAPPYness in as much detail as possible. These need to be your words, your feelings, your thoughts, your actions! No need to break out the dictionary to know what Happyness feels like to YOU. Write down the words as they come to you. It could be a few words that really resonate with you, it could be more of a description with a few sentences. Just make sure they are your true feelings of HAPPYness. We aren't here to impress anyone with Shakespearean poetry, unless of course, that is really how you feel! This is for you and your eyes only to help create another tool for you to use on this journey!

Being Happy is Classy

Day 10

DESERVE HAPPYness

I know I DESERVE HAPPYness! There is nothing in my past that will keep me from my HAPPYness. The more I know I deserve HAPPYness, the more I will attract. I keep positive thoughts in my head by saying, "I DESERVE HAPPYness"!

ACTION STEP

I absolutely believe you deserve HAPPYness, YOU must believe it too! Believe in the fact that you can be Happy, no matter your past (you need to let that go), and stay positive with yourself. I am a firm believer of self-improvement, which is the whole point of this workbook. By saying the words, "I deserve HAPPYness NOW," and believing these words as fact, means you're accepting yourself for who you are, but doesn't mean you stop trying to be a better you. This is not a competition with anyone but yourself. Embracing this from inside of you means you're ready to accept that you deserve it. Repeat as often as you can today . . . yell it if you want. :)

"I DESERVE HAPPYness NOW!"

"Whether you think you can or you think you can't, you are right."
—Henry Ford

I Know I CAN have HAPPYness.

Day 11

APPLY HAPPYness

I APPLY HAPPYness NOW, right this moment. There are seven days in the week and someday isn't one of them! Now is the perfect time to celebrate my HAPPYness.

ACTION STEP

APPLY what you've learned so far right NOW! This is about the present!

"I am happy because —", and fill in the blank. Are you alive? Are you healthy? Do you have a place to live? Do you have people who love you? Do you have all this and more? Then of course you can be happy now! Being happy with what you have NOW doesn't mean you're going to be "stuck" where you are at this moment. It just means you appreciate what you have.

Once you really appreciate what you have, this sense of gratitude will open pathways for more HAPPYness to come into your life, and quite possibly in different ways than you thought it would. Live with a grateful heart and APPLY HAPPYness NOW!

"Start where I am, Use what I have, Do what I can!"
—Arthur Ashe

Day 12

INITIATE HAPPYness

I INITIATE HAPPYness and make it a goal and target for myself! This is SO important. Make a goal/vision board with pictures that you can put up on your wall to look at and read EVERY day. Then make a plan to achieve it . . . this is your TARGET!

ACTION STEP

This may take a little more time, but please don't rush through this just to be done. Your goals must have meaning for you and make you feel good inside.

Make a goal/vision board that clearly has what you want to achieve on it. My family does this every December to prepare for the next new year. Our kids, from the time they were two years old, had goal boards with a big picture of a toilet in the middle for "Potty Training", the "ABC's" across the top and numbers 1-20 along the bottom of the board. It started with just a few things that we wanted to accomplish that year, and as they matured, their goals matured to getting good grades, making great friends, playing sports/activities, donating/community service, making money and saving money. As you continue your journey into adulthood, and learn about more opportunities out in the world, HOPEFULLY your goals expand too: finding that special person to spend the rest of your life with, creating a family, doing a job that you LOVE, maintaining a healthy lifestyle, opening your own business, even writing a book.

This list can literally be ANYTHING that moves you and feels good in your heart. Make this FUN for you to look at. Add some pictures, motivational quotes, Bible verses that move you, keeping this process simple and fun. You want your goals to push you while being achievable. I've had things on my board for a couple years before making it happen, and that's OK. I achieved it, finally, and it felt good!

I've also changed my mind before about my goals and have taken something off and replaced it with something else, because as you grow and change, your goals will grow and change too!

Now, when you've completed putting this together, hang it somewhere that you will see and read it every day. This is so important. Read them out loud and really visualize it all happening! Take it all into your heart and know this as your reality.

"Be the change I wish to see in the world."
—Mahatma Gandhi

Day 13

PRIORITIZE HAPPYness

I make HAPPYness my Priority!

Always try to continually put HAPPYness for yourself AND for others first by making it a PRIORITY in your life. Put yourself in good situations that will give you the best chance at HAPPYness. If there is someone in your life that may have a negative influence on you....STAY AWAY from them. It's your life and you get to say who you hang around.

ACTION STEP

OK, making yourself a priority may sound selfish to some people, but I can assure you it's not. By taking care of your needs, you can better serve the needs of others. This comes in many forms. How? Well let me give you a simple example.

Let's say you are in a service based industry......You are working in a restaurant, you didn't have a healthy lunch, in fact, you skipped lunch and just grabbed a cookie to "tide you over". Well, now you're energy is low, your tired, moving slowly and maybe a bit grumpy. You are serving your table and it's obvious to your customers that you aren't giving them the attention they are expecting. I bet that will reflect in your tip! OOPS......Now I hear the excuses coming!.... "Well I didn't have time to go get food."....Really? Let's figure this out together. PACK SOME HEALTHY FOOD before you leave the house. OH? You didn't have time this morning? Well then....plan your day. Say your goals. Pack healthy food.....All done in 15 min. Get up 15 min earlier!! You may think this is a cruel joke, but you'll be amazed at how much better your days will run if you PRIORITIZE your time so you can fulfill the HAPPYness goal you have just made for yourself. Taa Daa! Is 15 minutes less sleep worth a lifetime of amazingly Happy days? Thought so. You might like the way this feels so much that you may want to get up even earlier to get some "YOU TIME"! I enjoy getting up before everyone else in my house, and use this time to work on personal projects because this is when it is quiet. I also get to start every morning watching a beautiful sunrise. Now go plan out your day!

Do more of what makes me Happy!

Day 14

PRACTICE HAPPYness

A fun, simple smile may come easier to some than to others . . . so PRACTICE! Look into a mirror and practice a fun smile, stand up straight and walk with confidence. Soon, smiling and HAPPYness will be natural for you too.

BE someone who makes YOU Happy!

ACTION STEP

I understand this may sound silly, but don't tell me you've never practiced smiling or poses for picture day or a selfie! LOL, we ALL have! Now we are putting these actions to better use . . . to spread HAPPYness! OK, so I was watching the Dog Whisperer, and one day he said something that I'm sure most of us have heard before. When a dog's tail is down between their legs, they are fearful or intimidated by something (that part I knew). When the tail is carried in a normal (neutral) position, they have confidence (that I knew too). BUT, here's what I didn't know, a person can manually lift the dog's tail and that triggers the dog's confidence level. It's like a flip switch on a light! Now, imagine your smile being the switch. I'm not trying to compare you to a dog . . . not my intention, just comparing the action of confidence. OK, with that said, imagine your smile being the switch, and when you smile, it triggers endorphins that make you feel good, which in turn, gives you more confidence.

Smiling gives you a positive outlook on life, and because you feel better emotionally, then of course you will take even better care of your physical health. With all these wonderfully positive things going on within you = MORE HAPPYness!!
Yea for you! :)
SMILE!!! Everywhere you go . . . SMILE!!!
Walking down the street . . . SMILE! Driving in your car . . . SMILE! Riding your bike . . . SMILE! Looking at yourself in the reflection of a window as you pass by (I know you do) . . . SMILE! Keep that SMILE on your face all day. I'm not saying you have to show all your teeth all day long, but have a nice smile on your face, and then when you interact with others you can turn on the BIG SMILE. Here's another thing, I naturally have a downward turned "pouty" type of a mouth which can make my face look grumpy. I'm always thinking to myself to "SLIGHTY" turn the corners of my mouth up so I look more calm and HAPPY.

"Everyone SMILES in the same language!"
—George Carlin

Day 15

ATTRACT HAPPYness

Whatever you believe about yourself on the inside is what you will ATTRACT on the outside. Knowing you ARE HAPPYness is essential to ATTRACT it. The Law of Attraction is a powerful tool and one of the most important lessons in life. Unfortunately, so many don't use it, or simply don't know about it. There are many books explaining how this works. But, to put this as simple as possible, what this means is the energy you put into thinking about something, positively or negatively, is what you will get back. Even simpler, what you think about, you will bring about. This is also why those who set goals and read/visualize them every day usually get so much more done. When you see or read about someone who is doing really well in life, do you think they are sitting around and all these great things just happen to them? NO . . . they go for what they want! By having a positive mind, a loving heart and taking action they achieve what they do. I explained in the introduction of this workbook how this "Law" occurs to everyone at a certain level, you just didn't know what was happening. When you're thinking about someone, and then, that person calls or you see them somewhere, that's what this is — The Law of Attraction!!!

ACTION STEP

Today is going to be awesome! With every little thing you do today, you will put your new skill to work! From the time you're done reading this action step, think about every task you do and go into it with a positive attitude. You're going to feel so good when you're done completing your task or to do list, let this motivate you to do it happily. It has to be done anyway, so do it with a smile on your face. Make sure the corners of your mouth are pointed the right way. This doesn't mean everything is going to be perfect today, so don't get frustrated, just stay positive with your thoughts and see how close we come to MAKING our perfect day, by ATTRACTING it!

**Be so Happy that when others look at me
they become Happy too.**

Day 16

CREATE HAPPYness

I am responsible for my own HAPPYness, so I will CREATE it myself! Think about what will help make this process easier for you and create that space in your heart and with your positive mind set.

Design a life I love.

ACTION STEP

I'm sure you've heard the saying "Go to your Happy place" when you're having a tough go with something and trying to calm yourself. Well, why wait for adversity to go to your Happy place when you can create it and live there daily!

First, create a Happy Place in your mind by utilizing the tools in this workbook daily. I realize we are only halfway through our 30-day challenge, but everything you've learned so far is extremely powerful, and from here, we will continue to build your foundation for an incredibly Happy life.

Second, create your Happy place physically. Everyone enjoys a clean house, bedroom, car, closet, desk. Clean away the clutter! Get rid/donate what you don't need or use. Clutter will block your mind from growth, constricting your ability to fulfill what you truly want in your life. Clutter or messy drawers/cupboards can be overwhelming, and every time you look at it, your subconscious mind will be telling you to do something about it. By clearing your clutter, you essentially will be clearing your mind for better things in your life. Simplify your world to what you actually use. I really don't know how drawers can just suddenly get full of crap! Condense your odds and ends to one drawer, but keep it organized. There will come a day when you need that twist tie to hold something together. Now, you will know right where to find it!
Twice a year go through your house and purge and organize. I promise, the feeling of total organization will enhance your growth. You will be amazed at the opportunities that come knocking on your door when you don't have crap busting out and plenty of room to accept it. Knock knock. . . who's there . . . your HAPPYness!

Third, create a happy heart emotionally. We all have someone in our lives that just aren't healthy for us to be around EVERY day. Minimize those relationships. If they don't hold the positive qualities you're creating in your life right now, then find people who do! Now that you have all this positive energy to share, you will attract more positive people in your life. Change can be hard, but change is absolutely required for growth. Maybe you can share this workbook with them and they can grow too!

*"HAPPYness is not something you postpone for the future;
It is something you design for the present."*
—Jim Rohn

Day 17

SHARE HAPPYness

HAPPYness is just a word until I SHARE it with someone. Leave a little HAPPYness EVERYWHERE I go!

I have the power to make someone HAPPY today!

ACTION STEP

Ooooh, this is so important. We don't want to keep all this wonderful HAPPYness all to ourselves! Sharing with others always makes EVERYONE feel good. You (the giver), the receiver AND the watcher (if done in public), because sharing just makes the heart happy. I know you've heard...., "The more you give (HAPPYness), the more you receive (HAPPYness)". When this is done with true loving intention, our world will be open for more to come back to you.

My husband always says...., "The hole you get through is never bigger than the hole you give through." So true! BUT, this is NOT an exercise to see what you "get" out of it.   Your mind and heart will know the difference in your intentions. Do it for the love and joy of helping others feel good.

Here's another way, every morning each member of my family brings an inspirational, motivational, scripture passage or Happy thought to the breakfast table and we take turns reading them to each other and talk about what they mean to us. This is a fun way to start each day with positive words and encouragement.

I would rather be the person who smiled first
than the one who didn't smile at all.

Day 18

UNCOMPLICATE HAPPYness

You can engage your HAPPYness journey by keeping it UNCOMPLICATED and simple! Smile to a passerby, compliment someone, hold the door or buy a cup of coffee for someone. The point being, keep it simple at first and then you can get more creative.

ACTION STEP

Remember this is uncomplicated....keep it simple! If this is new for you, it's important to put yourself JUST outside of your comfort zone and still be willing to try this and have a good experience so you continue these simple actions.

I was raised and have lived in the country pretty much my whole life, and when I wanted to do some shopping, I would travel a couple hours away into, what Californians call, "The Bay Area". I was walking into the front door of a mall and noticed a woman with a toddler in one hand and carrying a smallish bag in the other. I opened the door and smiled, waiting a few seconds for her to enter. With a surprised look on her face (which I thought was odd) she thanked me as she walked through the doors. I said "Your welcome", she then stopped and turned to look at me and said, "You're not from here are you?", "How'd you know?" I replied, "People don't act like you here." Well.....then I had the surprised look on my face.   WHAT? All I did was open a door and smile!

Has our society really lost their manners? Have we gotten too busy to care? I HOPE NOT!!! Simple random acts of kindness can put a smile on someones face and change their day....so do it! Don't let the "Busyness" of our lives take our HAPPYness and keep us from sharing it with others. Let's bring HAPPYness back!

"Make it simple, but significant."
—Don Draper

Day 19

ACTIVATE HAPPYness

ACTIVATE HAPPYness in your life by surrounding yourself with pictures and people that make you smile. Read a book, spend time with a positive friend or go somewhere that will help activate the HAPPYness inside you.

ACTION STEP

A big part of activating HAPPYness within you is when your positive mind, positive heart and positive actions come together for the same purpose. Today we are going to draw! Don't worry, you don't have to be an artist for what we are about to do. I even made you an example below. To start, just draw these conjoining circles. Now, I didn't invent this circle art so you may have seen this before. It's used to help give people a visual of something, like we are about to do here. Now, write inside the circles what I have written. For those of you who are looking for your coloring pencils right now STOP! Stay on task....you can color when we are done. When you are finished with the circles take a second to really look at what you drew. In the middle of the conjoined circles of Mind (positive thoughts) and Body (Positive actions) is what? Your HEART which = YOUR HAPPYNESS! Ahhh Haaa!

Your heart is HAPPYest when your positive mind and positive body come together. Take a look at what is written outside the Mind and Body Circles. I wrote some simple examples that could apply to anyone because I really want you to get this! In a few POSITIVE words, starting with the mind circle, write down an affirmation. Then on the Body circle, write what you are going to do to keep this affirmation. Again, I suggest to KEEP THIS SIMPLE! Don't overwhelm yourself with a ton of things. Lets make 3 or less.....with total commitment. It's more important to accomplish 1 action first in the next 30 days then add another, rather than have too many and not do any of them because it's too much and feels overwhelming. Make a list of you want and prioritize them how you want to accomplish each one, then, use the top three on your list for this action step. This can also tie in real nicely with your goal/visual board. OK.....Now you can color :)

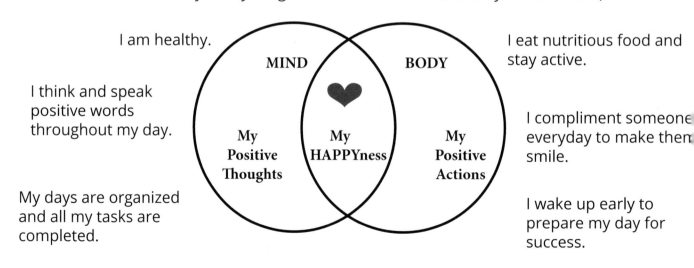

Remember that life is all about balance, whether we are talking about the Earth and her nature, or you and your life. The way you live your life and what you get out of it is directly proportional to what you put into it.....BALANCE!

Day 20

HABITUATE HAPPYness

By reading AND acting upon what you read in this workbook, you will begin to HABITUATE HAPPYness. Every day, you are training your mind, body and heart for this amazing emotion, and soon, it will become natural for you.

"HAPPYness doesn't mean everything is perfect. It means you've
decided to look beyond the imperfections."
—Gerard Way

ACTION STEP

You create habits, (good and bad) by practicing or feeding habits on a daily basis. So make HAPPYness YOUR habit. Practice your newly discovered habits you have learned in this workbook. Feed your HAPPYness with positive and motivating thoughts. Let's go back to day 1 and put the word "I" in front of the title page "Welcome HAPPYness".....Now it should read "I Welcome HAPPYness". Do this for every day we have completed so far, and as we continue on, you can do the same for each day to come. By writing "I" in front of the title of each page, it makes your mind understand and believe that ALL of this HAPPYness is because of what YOU are doing. YOU are creating your good habits to create your own HAPPYness.

If I change nothing then nothing will change.
I am cultivating HAPPYness in my life and making it a habit.

Day 21

APPRECIATE HAPPYness

Like a great relationship, the more you APPRECIATE your other half, the more your relationship grows and the better it gets!

HAPPYness is best when it's shared and appreciated.

ACTION STEP

By APPRECIATING HAPPYness, and committing yourself to sharing it with others.....This will complete a "Circle of HAPPYness". Life isn't meant to stay stationary, in one place without growth, and neither is HAPPYness! It's meant to be shared with others and also appreciated when you see it so this energy can come full circle. The more you share, the more it will come back to you completing the cycle. Today you are going to take some notes....Don't worry, you are just going to jot down actions you see others doing that makes you Happy whether it involves you or not. In a relationship, being appreciated feels good, and when appreciated, it makes you want to do more in return. If you can't write at that moment, make a mental note and put it in your workbook when you get the chance. Then, tonight, read what you observed out in the world today. You might have seen a driver let another driver in while sitting in traffic, or maybe, seeing a teenager helping an elderly person lift something into their shopping cart, or a fellow student picking up some trash that someone else had dropped.

When you apply yourself to making your relationship with HAPPYness better by seeing how others share it too, your "circle" will be enhanced because of your appreciation of its' works.

Day 22

LOVE HAPPYness

Like the saying "Love Conquers All", be so in LOVE with HAPPYness that NOTHING can stop this feeling. Want it so badly that you live, breathe, sleep, appreciate, visualize and share it every moment possible. I know this sounds impossible, however, the point is to try with every bit of yourself to make this happen and I know the faster you will see results.

ACTION STEP

LIVE—Start noticing all the simple things we can take for granted. Watch sunrises and sunsets, feel the rain on your skin and listen to the wind through the trees.

BREATHE—Close your eyes and take a deep breath, feel all of these tiny molecules of Happy faces being sucked into your lungs. Goofy.....but just do it! Let yourself be goofy, it's good for you!

SLEEP—Fall asleep thinking of positive things that are going to happen tomorrow starting with waking up with tons of energy to tackle your day.

SHARE—Keep up with the small acts of kindness that will make others Happy. You should be getting quite good at this by now.

VISUALIZE—Seeing (visualizing) what you want in life and do it with intention. Think about it, read it on your goal board, and see it happening to you.

APPRECIATE—Maintain your "Circle of HAPPYness" by seeing it around you and appreciating what others are doing too.

The HAPPYest people don't always have the best of everything, they just make the best of everything.

Day 23

TRAIN HAPPYness

Every day, I TRAIN for HAPPYness! We all love coming in first place.....so act how you want to be and train for first place. Keeping yourself on track with anything in your life takes discipline and training. You must be able to see the big AND the small details in your life that you can do better.....and then act on it. Being disciplined in the ways that don't come easy to us is HARD! This won't be easy, but it will be worth it. Your mind is a powerful tool that can do great things, but can also slip back into old habits, so you must train hard! The most important thing to remember is that YOU control your mind....YOU control your thoughts....YOU control your actions!

HAPPYness is GOOD for your health!

ACTION STEP

Training to win at something takes practicing your craft the right way and really noticing the details where you can improve. Find those areas you can get better at, the obvious AND the not so obvious.

Ask yourself these questions...

1.) What is something you know you aren't doing that you need to do?
2.) What is something you know you are already doing that you can do better?
3.) What is something you aren't even acknowledging that you can start doing?

Read each question again, then write down one thing in each category that you are going to do to become a better you. And Whala, just by acknowledging and writing down these things, you will now notice the smaller things that will help you train harder for your success!

The ones who are crazy enough to think they can change the world.....Are the ones that DO!

Let's change the world with HAPPYness!

Day 24

EMBRACE HAPPYness

I EMBRACE HAPPYness and I am comfortable with it. The more you are willing to open yourself up and embrace this incredible energy, the faster you will receive it. You deserve to have this, so embrace it with you ALWAYS!

ACTION STEP

I know you are on a mission to finish this workbook and I hope you are having fun with this. PLEASE don't rush through these steps just to be done. Embrace everyday of your HAPPYness Challenge and feed this amazing energy from all aspects of your life. Embrace the fact that you decided to take this 30 day journey. Embrace the fact that you are doing each day with intent. Embrace the fact that you are feeling and seeing a difference in your life, and embrace the fact that you are seeing more HAPPYness around you! Take it ALL in and embrace every moment!

I can never have too much HAPPYness.

Day 25

OWN HAPPYness

When you own something, it gives you a certain sense of pride, hence the term...Pride of Ownership.

Knowing that it's yours gives you a certain feeling that no one can take away from you. It's not boastful or bragging. Being proud of something you have and worked for is a good thing and should be treated with care.

This is how your HAPPYness should be taken care of! It's yours to OWN and yours to share with whomever you want. No one can take this from you because your HAPPYness doesn't depend on what others do. So OWN it and give it freely!

Have SO much HAPPYness that when others look at you they get HAPPY too.

HAPPYness is a form of courage.

ACTION STEP

You are becoming a new positive, stronger, healthier, HAPPYer you! Own this about yourself! Have confidence in yourself.....your body language tells a lot about you! STAND UP STRAIGHT **AND** SIT UP STRAIGHT!! I know I sound like a mom right now and that's fine, let me be your mom for two minutes while you read this. Standing up straight is what will keep you healthier longer! Your spine is the foundation for which your body thrives. KIDS LISTEN UP!!! This is so very important for your health, especially as you become adults. While you are growing, your bones, muscles and vital organs go through stages of growth. During these stages of your life you are making your body create its own habits by telling it how to grow. If you are always hunched over, imagine a "C", then as you grow, your bones and muscles will take that shape permanently. This causes your vital organs (heart, lungs, stomach etc) to squish together. Which means, not as much oxygen taken into the lungs because they can't fully expand, not as much room for your heart to beat normally, no freedom of movement for your stomach and intestines causing digestive problems like constipation and acid reflux. No, I am not a doctor. However, it does not take a doctor to understand health at this level when explained simply. When you see someone all hunched over and crooked, imagine their organs squished together not able to function the way they should because it is now all crowded inside.....Do you think they could live a healthier life if they were able to stand up straight and tall giving all of their organs room to perform at their best? How do you envision yourself in your future? If you are having a hard time picturing the human body then look one up and see for yourself.
Put the time into your spine and STAND UP STRAIGHT! Now, can you guess what your action step is today? Keep reminding yourself.....Tie a piece of colored string around your wrist and every time you look at it, you take in a deep breath, put your shoulders back and lift your chin up. This too will take time, but you will retrain all these muscles to pull your spine into the healthy position it was meant to be in. Now go out and OWN your day with confidence AND health the way it should be because your body feels better, then of course you will be HAPPYer!

Which person looks healthier and more confident?

Your spine is your foundathion and you only get one!

Day 26

REFLECT HAPPYness

I REFLECT HAPPYness in everything I do, even in the simplest of things. Because how I do one thing, is how I do everything.

"The art of HAPPYness is being able to extract it from the common things."
—Henry Ward Beecher

ACTION STEP

Is there one thing on your "To Do" list that you have been procrastinating to do? Now's the time to do it! Think how you are going to feel when this project is DONE! You are going to do this with a smile on your face and excitement in your heart because you will not have this in the back of your mind anymore taking up valuable HAPPY space. Procrastination is a HORRIBLE habit that most of us have battled with at one point in our lives, or continue to battle every day. Let's work on changing that RIGHT NOW. We are going to commit to this project until it's complete, and use the HAPPYness you are going to feel when it's done as encouragement to finish.

Success Loves Action!

"Ever since HAPPYness heard your name it has been looking for YOU!"
—Hafiz

Day 27

LEAD HAPPYness

To be able to LEAD HAPPYness is one of the best gifts you can share with someone. To be a leader and show others how HAPPYness looks and feels can be one of life's most valuable lessons.   And all they have to do is watch you....

Be the reason someone smiles today!

ACTION STEP

The best type of Leadership is leading by example, because actions will ALWAYS speak louder than words. Be the best "Happy You" you can be so others can see the change in you and want that change for themselves! Be on your HAPPYness game today and show those watching you that life is so much more incredible when you are HAPPY!

Lead by example....Follow by choice. Just make sure you choose to follow the right people!

Because I knew you, I have been changed for the better.

Day 28

EMPOWER HAPPYness

You have been dedicated to your HAPPYness and have almost completed this 30 day challenge. Your friends and family have seen the difference in you, and with the tools you have learned during this process, you can share this journey with others. If you haven't already, think of a person (or two) to EMPOWER with this wonderful experience. By giving this workbook to someone and sharing with them the tools that you have learned, then they too, can start to feel the power of HAPPYness!

ACTION STEP

You have the ability to CHANGE someones life right now! That's Huge! Gift a copy of this workbook to someone and tell them how it has changed your life! Empower someone with the gift of HAPPYness and watch them grow!

Because I CAN!

Day 29

MAINTAIN HAPPYness

Just because you completed this workbook doesn't mean you are done, oh no, no, no. You are going to MAINTAIN HAPPYness in your life! Yes, it will take work, but it will be worth your effort. Don't limit your HAPPYness to 30 days....Find more fun ways to encourage it to others.... See it and appreciate it more often to complete your circle! This circle is continuous, it has no beginning and it has no end. Just keep moving forward to MAINTAIN what you have learned. You never know who needs you.....and HAPPYness is contagious.

ACTION STEP

Keep going! You have created some amazing new habits by now to help you continue this journey forever! It will take some work, yes, that is why this is called a workbook, but, it's the actions needed to maintain you moving in a positive direction of HAPPYness. Love the life of HAPPYness you now own, but continually work on more! Re-read this workbook as much as you want and keep your HAPPYness journey perpetually moving forward! You Got This!

Be the type of person you would want to meet.

Here is a visual of Maintaining HAPPYness. This letter "Z" concept shows how you can continue to grow even when you "Get All You Want"! Keep reaching! This diagram starts from the bottom line and, of course, work your way up! ;)

Letter "Z" of Life

The Bottom Line represents No Growth in your life. You don't make goals, you don't seek to better yourself. You let life "happen" to you and just go with the flow of the current like so many others that don't have dreams they want to actively attain.

The strong upward Middle Line represents your life with extreme growth! You just learned how to motivate yourself with goals and have ambitions and set higher standards for yourself. This excitement creates a vacuum effect and as you stay on track, you will create huge growth in your life. You learned how to use new tools AND you implement these ideas by taking action!

The straight Top Line represents you fulfilling your goals and dreams and now you think, "What else is there?". You've settled into the wonderful life you've made and are Happy where you are. That can totally be enough for you, but maybe there's more!

The slightly upward stepped Line represents this "I think there's more"! This part of peoples lives will come at different stages for everyone. You can always continue to grow yourself in many ways. Keeping your mind and body in an active state of growth is key to living a longer HAPPYer life! You will always find more if you continue to look.

REMEMBER....
This entire Letter Z has no time line! Please don't compare your life to others, just let others inspire you! The only person you are trying to be better than is the person you were yesterday ;) Stay positive to yourself and let your hunger to want to be a better you fuel your fire!

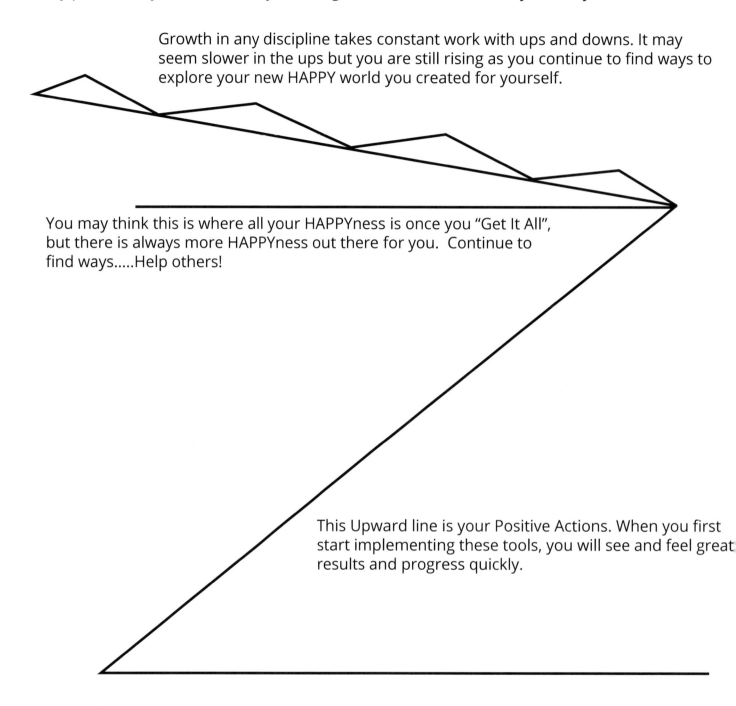

Growth in any discipline takes constant work with ups and downs. It may seem slower in the ups but you are still rising as you continue to find ways to explore your new HAPPY world you created for yourself.

You may think this is where all your HAPPYness is once you "Get It All", but there is always more HAPPYness out there for you. Continue to find ways.....Help others!

This Upward line is your Positive Actions. When you first start implementing these tools, you will see and feel great results and progress quickly.

Staying where you are - No Growth
This is where you start in life, but you don't have to finish here. By finding ways to better yourself, no matter how small, it all counts to bring you higher and farther than where you started.
JUST START!

Day 30

LIVE HAPPYness

Every day in every way LIVE your life with HAPPYness! It's completely up to you because YOU are in control of your own HAPPYness.

"Wherever I go.....No matter the weather..... I ALWAYS bring my own sunshine!"

ACTION STEP

I LOVE this saying.....ALWAYS bring your own sunshine! See the lesson in every situation and then let your sun shine down to fill it with HAPPYness.

Now, if you have REALLY put forth the effort with everything described in this book for YOUR HAPPYness, I know you have seen and felt wonderful changes in your life. Remember, in these pages are tools, but like any tool, YOU must put it into action for them to work. A hammer can hammer a nail, but YOU need to swing it. YOU must put the tools mentioned in this book into action for yourself before anything will come of it. If for some reason you don't feel like you have put forth your BEST effort to accomplish what is in this workbook.....DO IT AGAIN! It's that simple...Another 30 days!

BELIEVE in yourself and in your ability to achieve whatever you want. Write down your goals AND make a visual goal board you can look at EVERY DAY! Put pictures on it and words of encouragement to make it exciting for you. Remember, once your mind is expanded by a new idea it should never regain its original shape.

I want to leave you with something very valuable for you to think about. You know that each daily challenge is a tool for you to propel you forward to a certain goal...in this case specifically, HAPPYness. Now that you understand how it works, and this part is extremely important for you to understand.....you can replace this word with ANYTHING you want to achieve and USE THE SAME TOOLS and daily challenges in this workbook to get you there!!! HAPPYness is the first important step to help give you a push in the right direction for your journey. With HAPPYness on your side, and these tools, you WILL achieve all you set your mind to!

WHAT YOU BELIEVE.....YOU CAN ACHIEVE!

HAPPYness......Rated "E" for Everyone!

Notes & Positive Personal Reflections

Made in United States
Troutdale, OR
06/19/2024

20630893R00026